D0229441

First published 2012 by Walker Books Ltd
87 Vauxhall Walk, London SE11 5HJ

2 4 6 8 10 9 7 5 3 1

© 2012 Brun Limited

The right of Anthony Browne to be identified as author/illustrator of this work has been asserted by him in accordance
with the Copyright, Designs and Patents Act 1988

This book has been typeset in New Century Schoolbook

Printed in China

British Library Cataloguing in Publication Data:
a catalogue record for this book is available from the British Library

ISBN 978-1-4063-2579-9

www.walker.co.uk

WALKER BOOKS
AND SUBSIDIARIES
LONDON • BOSTON • SYDNEY • AUCKLAND

ANTHONY BROWNE

One Gorilla

A Counting Book

1

Gorilla

2
Orang-utans

3
Chimpanzees

Mandrills

5
Baboons

6
Gibbons

7 Spider

Monkeys

8 Macaques

9

Colobus
Monkeys

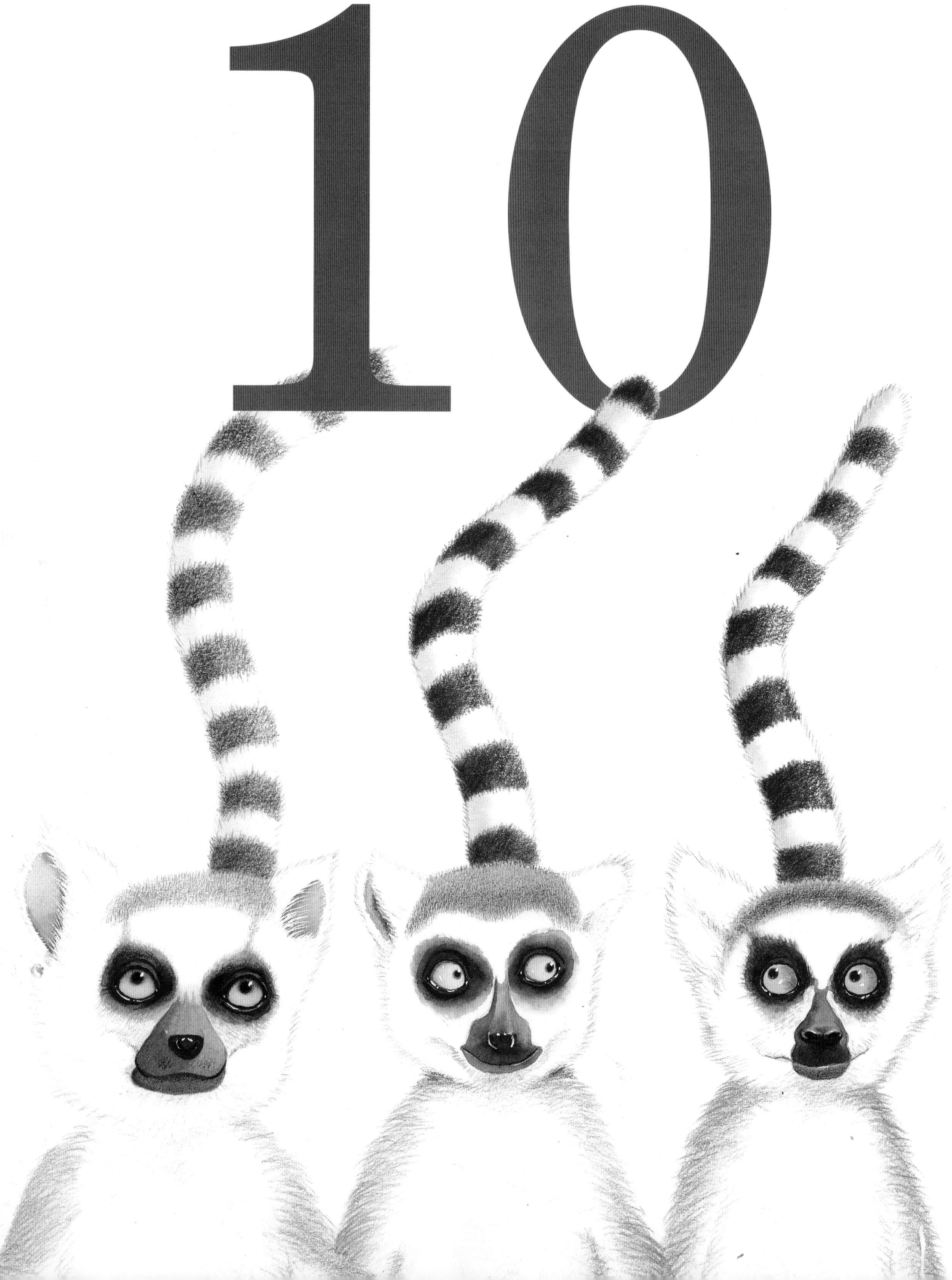
10

Lemurs

All Primates.
All one family.
All my family...

And yours!